The hare-kin

HARE

written by Zoë Greaves

Illustrated by Leslie Sadleir

Old Barn
Books

He is coming! O'Hare is coming this way!

Call him Hare King.

The hare-kin

 O'Hare's a hare; a golden hare, as rare a hare as any hare could be.

The swift-as-wind
The frisky one

Quiet now. You must not make a sound. Quieter still.

Can you hear a hare's breath?

Hide here in the scrub.

The low creeper

Look now. Look carefully.

Look still more harefully.

The stag of the cabbages

Long-eared

O where, O where is O'Hare?

Don't confuse him with a rabbit.

Hare was born with his clothes on, eyes wide and ready to go.

The dew-hopper

The dew-beater

Nobody knows where he goes!

Hare today, gone tomorrow!

The cropper of herbage

Hare
here?

The hopper in the grass

Hare there?
HERE HARE!

The light-foot

Old Big-bum

O'Hare is here! Leaping there! Magnificent hare!

O'Hare hears. *The get-up quickly*

The fidgety-footed one

He was hare…

and now he's gone.

The fellow in the dew

The slink-away

Heir to the moon.

The Stag of the Cabbages

Hares are wild creatures which have tended to live close to people on moorland or farmland. Yet even though we are such close neighbours, humans haven't ever managed to understand all of the hare's secrets. We appear to have complex feelings toward the hare – a mixture of awe, affection and fear.

To us, hares are mysterious and full of contradictions – all at once comical and regal. One minute timid, the next bold, verging on "bonkers". They are mostly solitary and nocturnal creatures.

Though they have been seen to gather in huge numbers on runways where they appear to enjoy racing aeroplanes as they prepare for take-off!

For most of the year you'll not see a single one, then suddenly in the spring they'll appear in droves, brazenly leaping about the open countryside. Where do they come from? Where do they go? There are about 32 different species of hare in the world today and they live on every continent except Antarctica. The most common is the brown hare or European hare – but you might also see a snowshoe hare (white all year round), a golden hare, a jackrabbit, a broom hare, a Hainan hare, an Arctic hare, or a mountain hare (white in the winter) – to name a few.

The Moon Hares

On a clear night, if you look carefully, you might be able to make out the shape of a hare on the moon. And when you do this you are doing something that people have been doing all around the world for thousands of years.

The moon and the hare appear together in myth and folklore in India, China, Africa, North America and Europe.

Bhuddists have a saying about "seeing the shadow of a hare in the moon", like the Western "man in the moon".

Sanskrit and Singalese tales tell of the *Palace of the King of the Hares* on the moon. Hindus called the moon Sasanka, which means "marked with the hare."

In China, the moon hare mixed a magical elixir of life for the goddess Chang'e. Chang'e floated off to live on the moon after stealing a pill of immortality!

Many moon goddesses are associated with hares. One shape-shifter goddess from Siberia called Kaltes often turned herself into a hare. The Norse goddess Freyja has hare attendants. In Britain, the moon goddess Andraste was also linked to the hare and Bouddica the Queen of the Iceni invoked the protection of Andraste before she went into battle against the invading Romans. Boudicca released a hare from her gowns and since the hare ran in an auspicious direction the entire Iceni army raised a mighty battle cry, confident of victory.

In Africa, the hare was considered part of the moon. One myth that appears all over Africa tells that when the earth was created the moon was so pleased that she wanted to give mankind the gift of immortality. So she sent the hare to pass on the message "Just as the moon dies and rises again so shall you." But the hare got the message muddled-up and instead passed on "Just as the moon dies and perishes, so shall you." The earth people believed the hare's words and they became mortal. The moon was furious and beat the hare. The blow slit the hare's mouth to a hare-lip. The hare fled and is still fleeing! In some versions the hare and the moon eventually make friends again

Tales of the Hare

From Africa to North America, from the Far East to Europe, for many thousands of years people have been telling each other stories about the hare in mythology, religion and folktale.

Eostra (sounds like 'Easter') was a Celtic goddess of the dawn and her favourite animal was the hare. Eostra even turned into a hare at the full moon.

The closely-linked Anglo-Saxon goddess Ostara is depicted with hare's ears – sometimes with an entire hare's head. She is a goddess of spring, fertility and resurrection.

It is believed that, once, to please the children of the world, Ostara changed her pet bird into a hare. This hare laid brightly coloured eggs, which she gave to the children as presents. This is why, in Europe, the Easter bunny lays eggs at Easter time. It's not a bunny – it's a hare!

The story of the tortoise and the hare from Aesop's Fables is very well known. In this the hare is so confident of his speed he thinks he'll easily beat the slow tortoise. The hare bounds off ahead but is easily distracted along the way – eventually stopping completely for a snooze! The slow and steadfast tortoise wins the race… but I'd rather hang out with the madcap wild hare than the ever-reliable (and distinctly duller) tortoise.

There are also plenty of stories around the world that feature a young woman who can shape-shift into a hare. Very often some brave and handsome hero, while out hunting, wounds a hare – but the hare miraculously escapes. Sometime later the hero will discover a beautiful young woman with an eerily similar wound in her leg!

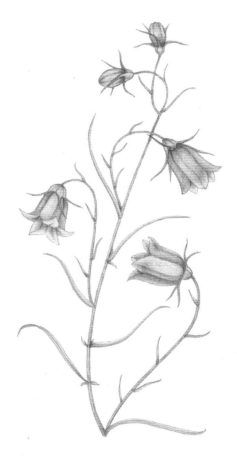

Native American hares

Throughout Algonquin culture the hare appears as a powerful hero. The first creator, the maker of the sun, moon and earth is called Michabo or The Great White Hare. Michabo has many talents – he is the ruler of the winds, mists, thunder and lightening, chief of all the animals, the guardian of the people, the inventor of picture writing and a shape-shifter.

It hasn't always been all-powerful plain sailing for Michabo. When he first tried his hand at creation he made a mistake and accidentally flooded the world. Realising he'd now have to start all over again he asked for help, but none of his friends, like the Raven or the Otter, could help him. Finally the Muskrat dived down to the bottom of the sea and returned with a paw full of mud – from which Michabo was able to create the earth.

Another hare god was Manabozho – closely linked to Michabo – in fact sometimes they change places, depending on which legend you read.

Manabozho was a trickster god who amused himself by playing games with mortals. He was a bit of a rogue – always causing trouble and impossible to beat. He was, unsurprisingly, in charge of mayhem! Basically a good soul, he loved his brothers dearly. One brother, Wabasso, chose to spend a good deal of his life hanging out with the northern spirits and through them he learned about medicine. Manabozho, being kind, wrote all this knowledge of medicine down and gave it to the mortals as a gift.

Manabozho's other beloved brother was the wolf-like Chibiaos. One day an evil spirit melted the ice that Chibiaos was walking on. Chibiaos drowned and ended up in the underworld.

Manabozho spent six years struggling against the evil spirits to get his brother back. He finally won – using his wit – and the evil spirits allowed Chibiaos to return as protector of the dead.

Manabozho later reappeared as Bre'r Rabbit – see Trickster Hares!

Trickster Hares – cunning, witty, fast and clever

All across the world tales of the trickster abound – these are tales of cunning, of bravery, of cleverness and deceit. The trickster hero tends to take the role of the "fool" and is distinguished by his wit and cleverness, or his plain old craziness! Tricksters weren't actually foolish or crazy – these heroes just saw the world differently and could often save the day by using their unique vision. Their irreverent behaviour and willingness to break rules often helped them raise awareness or shed light on injustice.

In West Africa, *The Pulling Contest* and *Hare Goes Hunting with Hyena* are well-known trickster tales. In Zambia, the hare is called Kalulu and in Nigeria the Hausa people tell the tale of the King of Beasts, who is a hare.

These tales travelled from Africa to America during the years of slave trading and over time they combined with the Native American Algonquin tales to become the famous adventures of Bre'r Rabbit – a jackrabbit, which is an American hare.

In this light, Bre'r Rabbit becomes a vital character – a true hero of folklore and the world. Although smaller than his enemies and apparently weaker, he continually outwits and outsmarts his more powerful foes Bre'r Bear, Bre'r Wolf and Bre'r Fox.

Bre'r Rabbit wasn't really a rabbit as there are no rabbits in Africa – only hares! Bugs Bunny is also a hare – not a rabbit! And a zany, flippant trickster!

Lucky Hares

In China, the hare was considered the guardian of all wild animals and, along with the phoenix and unicorn, was believed to bring luck and prosperity. A green jade figure of a hare would be carried for luck.

In ancient Egypt, the Hare was often shown greeting the dawn. The hieroglyphic "Wn" depicts a hare on top of a single blue-green ripple and means "to exist."

One it is ill luck to meet

During the middle ages, poachers, when hunting the hare, would recite a poem of 72 names for the hare to ward off ill omens because in pre-Christian times hunting the hare was considered so taboo that even to speak its true name would bring bad luck.

Hares (along with cats) were associated with witchcraft and many people believed witches could turn themselves into hares – as a result they were often thought to bring bad luck.

Sailors would return home if a hare crossed their path when they were setting out for their boats.

A girl would postpone her wedding if a hare crossed her path during her engagement.

It was considered unlucky for a pregnant woman to see a hare.

Mad as a March Hare

During Christian times, as part of a greater attempt to suppress long-held pagan beliefs, the hare became a harbinger of bad luck or death. Their godlike name in tatters, hares became associated with frivolity and madness – because of their crazy behaviour in the spring, when large numbers of hares can be seen leaping and boxing. And, rather than being considered messengers of the gods or divinely inspired, they were said to resemble a coven of witches dancing.

To be "mad as a March hare" has been a common expression since the 16th century and was most famously celebrated by Lewis Carroll in *Alice in Wonderland* with the March Hare – as unstable and alarming as his companion the Mad Hatter!

10 Hare facts

1. Fast and Agile
Hares can reach speeds of up to 45 mph and they can keep up this speed over long distances. They can leap an amazing 2m vertically and suddenly change direction. Few predators can match this pace and agility. Usually the only hares that are caught are the old, injured or very young.

2. Powerful
They drum on the ground with their hind feet to warn of danger. They can use their powerful legs and feet to kick an enemy.

3. Nocturnal
Hares are mostly nocturnal, venturing out at night to nibble on vegetation.

4. Fertile
Hares breed between February and September every year. Female hares, or does, can give birth to 42 babies in their lifetime – which is perhaps why ancient people associated them with fertility.

5. Solitary
Hares are mostly solitary. They don't have a permanent home but move about the countryside, sleeping where they can find camouflage.

At certain times of the year, especially in the Spring and Summer, they will gather in large numbers to mate or play.

A group of hares is called a 'drove'.

6. Silent
They make very little noise. Mother hares make soft grunting noises when they communicate with their babies. But if they are very frightened, they will scream.

7. Leverets
Hares give birth to their young out in the open. Hares under a year old are called leverets. They are born covered in fur and with their eyes open. After just a few minutes they can hop about.

8. Alert
A hare's eyes are placed on the sides of its head – so they can see danger in front and to the side at the same time. Their large ears can move independently so the hare can hear sounds and possible dangers from all around.

9. Herbivores
Hares are mainly herbivores – meaning they eat plants and their diet changes seasonally depending on what is available.

10. Boxing
In February and March male hares start to follow females around. Male hares will compete – the stronger males driving off the weaker males. When the successful males finally make their approaches, the females will very often hit them with their front feet. No-one knows exactly why.

This is called "boxing". It looks very dramatic but the hares are rarely injured.

What's the difference
between a hare and a rabbit?

Brown hares have black tips on their ears – rabbits do not.

Hares can swim. Rabbits cannot.

Hares have long legs – rabbits' legs are mostly hidden.

Hares run fast over long distances while rabbits just scamper about.

Hares eat in the middle of large fields – rabbits feed close to their warrens, in woods or hedgerows.

Brown hares have a black stripe on the top of their tail –rabbits do not.

Hares do not dig underground dens like rabbits – they spend their lives above ground, even when asleep. They make shallow dips called 'forms' – although nothing more than a depression in the grass, hares will be well hidden from enemies.

Acknowledgements

"Hare" was originally inspired by the poetry of William Cowper (1731-1800)
and a fortuitous encounter with a huge, handsome hare on the outskirts of a wood in Worcester.
Which was more like being visited by a king. I later read a translation, from Middle English, of "The Names of The Hare".
These names, a mix of descriptive, respectful and insulting were recited by superstitious poachers for success and protection.
Zoe Greaves

This book is for V&B from Z&L

Moral Rights:
Leslie Sadleir has asserted her right under the Copyright, Designs and Patents Act 1988
to be identified as Illustrator of this Work

AN OLD BARN BOOK
First published 2014 by IctisBooks
This edition published 2015 by Old Barn Books Ltd
www.oldbarnbooks.com
Illustration © 2015 Leslie Sadleir
Text © 2015 Zoe Greaves

ISBN: 978-1-91064-603-8

10 9 8 7 6 5 4 3 2 1

Printed in Malaysia